This Book Is Lovingly Presented to My Mother,

[redacted]

For My Mother

An Album of Memories

Ideals Children's Books • Nashville, Tennessee

Published by Ideals Children's Books
An imprint of Hambleton-Hill Publishing, Inc.
Nashville, Tennessee 37218

Printed and bound in the United States of America

ISBN 1-57102-028-4

The display type is set in Ingenius and Cochin.
The text type is set in Cochin.
Color separations were made by Wisconsin Technicolor, Inc.,
Pewaukee, Wisconsin.
Printed and bound by Worzalla Publishing,
Stevens Point, Wisconsin.

Dear Mother,

Please accept this gift of love, a book of memories from me to you.

I hope this collection of memories will show you how much you have always meant to me.

Love,

[redacted]

Early Childhood

Mother's arms are made of tenderness, and sweet sleep blesses the child who lies therein.

—Victor Hugo

My earliest memory . . .

I can still see you . . .

My favorite time with you was . . .

I especially loved it when we played . . .

Le berceau

Things to Remember

I always loved to hear you read . . .

My favorite story was . . .

My favorite toy was . . .

Remember those pet names . . .

Stories first heard
at a mother's knee
are never wholly
forgotten,
—a little spring
that never quite
dries up in our
journey through
scorching years.

—Giovanni Ruffini

Things to Remember

Do you remember that song . . .

You wanted me to eat vegetables, but my favorite food was . . .

Special traditions we shared . . .

How dear to this
heart are the scenes
of my childhood,
When fond
recollection presents
them to view.

—Samuel Woodworth

Maternal Kiss

A Mother's Touch

When I was sick, you made everything better by . . .

If I was frightened . . .

When I was sad . . .

I felt so special when . . .

Blessed be the hand

that prepares a

pleasure for a child,

for there is no

saying when and

where it may

bloom forth.

—Douglas Jerrold

photos or mementos

Birthday Memories

A special birthday cake . . .

My best birthday present . . .

Memorable birthdays . . .

Presents I gave you . . .

The heart of the giver makes the gift dear and precious.

—Martin Luther

The Spielers

My Favorite Stories about Your Childhood

Tell me the tales

that to me

were so dear,

Long, long ago,

long, long ago.

—Thomas Haynes Bayly

On the Balcony, Meudon

About You and Me

You and I are alike in these ways . . .

You and I are different in these ways . . .

By watching you, I learned . . .

Backward, turn

backward, O Time,

in thy flight;

Make me a child

again, just

for tonight.

—Elizabeth Akers Allen

photos or mementos

Our Family

My impressions of members of our family . . .

And so do his sisters

and his cousins

and his aunts!

His sisters and

his cousins

Whom he reckons

up by dozens,

And his aunts!

—William S. Gilbert

Our Family

More impressions and memories . . .

The happiest

moments of my life

have been the few

which I have passed

at home in the

bosom of my family.

—Thomas Jefferson

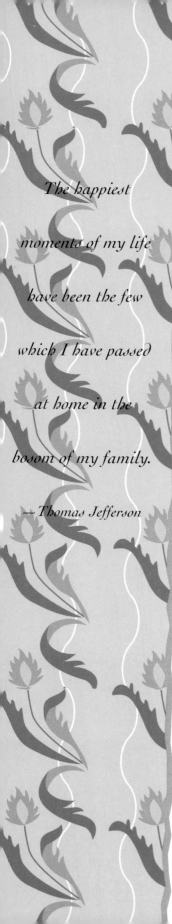

photos or mementos

Images of Home

There is a magic in

that little word,

home;

it is a mystic circle

that surrounds

comforts and virtues

never known beyond

its hallowed limits.

—Robert Southey

Home was always the place . . .

What I liked most about my room was . . .

I knew when you were home because . . .

You made our home special by . . .

Family Pets

My very first pet . . .

My favorite pet . . .

More about pets . . .

Animals are such agreeable friends — they ask no questions, they pass no criticisms.

—George Eliot

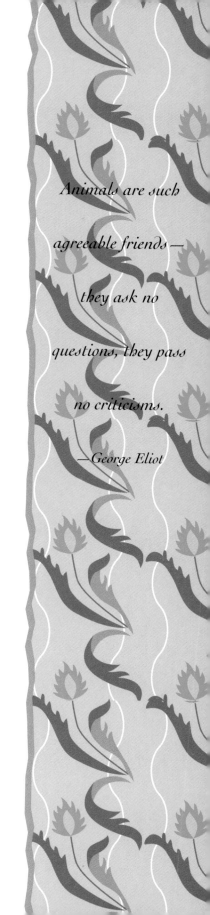

May Day, Central Park

Holidays

Favorite holidays . . .

Family traditions . . .

Every year, you and I . . .

A light heart

lives long.

—William Shakespeare

Holidays

I will never forget the year that . . .

My favorite gift from you . . .

One very special holiday memory is . . .

Remembered joys
are never past;
at once the fountain,
stream, and sea,
they were, they are,
they yet shall be.
—James Montgomery

Vacation Days

My favorite vacation memory is . . .

The worst vacation was . . .

I'll never forget the time . . .

May you live all the

days of your life.

—Jonathan Swift

School Days

My favorite subject was . . .

But I hated . . .

My favorite teachers . . .

My school friends . . .

The mother's heart is the child's schoolroom.

—Henry Ward Beecher

And Then There Was High School

High school was . . .

My favorite subject . . .

But I hated . . .

My teachers . . .

My friends . . .

After school, I . . .

Keep true

to the dreams

of thy youth.

—Johann von Schiller

Five O'Clock Tea

Growing Up: My Teenage Years

Do you remember . . .

I can't believe that I . . .

The craziest fad . . .

What the daughter does, the mother did.

—Jewish Proverb

Memorable Firsts

You cannot teach a child to take care of himself unless you will let him try to take care of himself. He will make mistakes; and out of these mistakes will come his wisdom.

—Henry Ward Beecher

The first time you let me stay home alone . . .

My first date . . .

The first time you let me drive the car . . .

My first job . . .

Another first . . .

Gloucester Farm

The Real Story

My mother had a great deal of trouble with me but I think she enjoyed it.

—Samuel Clemens

I know that you always thought . . .

I never told you . . .

You never knew the whole story of . . .

You didn't know that I knew . . .

Remember When . . .

Happiness was . . .

My biggest worry was . . .

A special day together was . . .

What the heart has

once owned and had,

it shall never lose.

—Henry Ward Beecher

photos or mementos

Laughter

Remember how we laughed when . . .

I know you wanted to laugh when . . .

It was so funny when . . .

A good laugh is sunshine in a house.

—William Makepeace Thackeray

The Little Things

These are the simple, everyday things that showed me you cared . . .

Life is made up, not of great sacrifices or duties, but of little things, in which smiles and kindness and small obligations, given habitually, are what win and preserve the heart and secure comfort.

—Sir Humphrey Davy

Things We Said

Remember how we said . . .

You always said . . .

The most important thing you told me . . .

And when she spake,

Sweet words,

like dropping honey,

she did shed;

And 'twixt the

pearls and rubies,

softly brake

A silver sound that

heavenly music

seem'd to make.

—Edmund Spenser

Special Friends

The ornament of a house is the friends who frequent it.

—Ralph Waldo Emerson

Corn-Shelling

photos or mementos

Leaving Home

College . . .

Marriage . . .

New places to live . . .

Things to look forward to . . .

No bird soars too high if he soars with his own wings.

—William Blake

Hopes and Dreams

Hope is like the sun, which, as we journey toward it, casts the shadow of our burden behind us.

—Samuel Smiles

I always wanted to be . . .

When I grew up, I was going to . . .

Because of you, today I am . . .

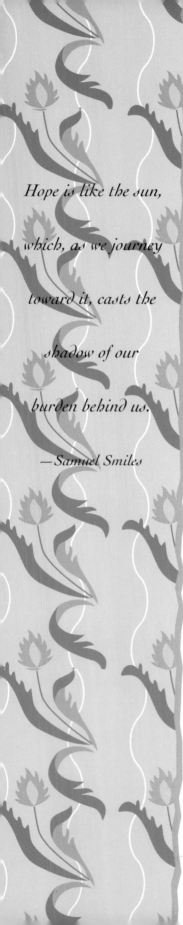

You May Not Have Known . . .

You influenced me by . . .

I was proud of you when . . .

I always loved it when . . .

You were always the person I could . . .

Blessed is the

influence of one true,

loving human soul

on another.

—George Eliot

I Love You

All that I am, or hope to be, I owe to my angel mother.

—Abraham Lincoln

I want to thank you for . . .

I promise . . .

In the years to come, I hope that you and I . . .

Boston at Common Twilight

Credits

Le berceau, 1872
BERTHE MORISOT
(FRENCH, 1841–1895)
Oil on canvas, 18 1/4" x 22" (46cm x 56cm)
Courtesy of Musée d'Orsay, Paris
Photo: © RMN

Boston at Common Twilight, 1885–6
FREDERICK CHILDE HASSAM
(AMERICAN, 1859–1935)
Oil on canvas, 42" x 60"
(106.7 x 152.4 cm)
Gift of Miss Maud E. Appleton
Courtesy, Museum of Fine Arts, Boston, Massachusetts

Corn-Shelling, 1864
EASTMAN JOHNSON
(AMERICAN, 1824–1906)
Oil on academy board, 15 3/8" x 12 1/2"
(39.3cm x 31.7cm)
Courtesy of The Toledo Museum of Art, Toledo, Ohio
Gift of Florence Scott Libbey

Five O'Clock Tea, ca. 1880
MARY CASSATT
(AMERICAN, 1844–1926)
Oil on canvas, 25 1/2" x 36 1/2"
(64.8cm x 92.7cm)
Courtesy, Museum of Fine Arts, Boston, Massachusetts
M. Theresa B. Hopkins Fund

Cover:
Gabrielle et Jean, 1895
PIERRE-AUGUSTE RENOIR
(FRENCH, 1841–1919)
Oil on canvas
Courtesy of Musée de l'Orangerie, Paris
Photo: © RMN

Gloucester Farm, 1874
WINSLOW HOMER
(AMERICAN, 1836–1910)
Oil on canvas, 20 3/4" x 30 1/8"
Philadelphia Museum of Art
Purchased: John H. McFadden Collection

Maternal Kiss, 1897
MARY CASSATT
(AMERICAN, 1844–1926)
Pastel on paper, 22" x 18 1/2"
Philadelphia Museum of Art
Bequest of Anne Hinchman

May Day, Central Park, 1901
MAURICE PRENDERGAST
(AMERICAN, 1858–1924)
Watercolor, 35.4cm x 50.6cm
Copyright © 1994 The Cleveland Museum of Art, Cleveland, Ohio
Gift from J. H. Wade, 26.17

On the Balcony, Meudon, 1874
BERTHE MORISOT
(FRENCH, 1841–1895)
Watercolor, with touches of gouache, over graphite, on off-white wove paper, 20.6cm x 17.3 cm
Gift of Mrs. Charles Netcher in memory of Charles Netcher II, 1933.1
Photo: © 1994 The Art Institute of Chicago. All Rights Reserved.

The Spielers, 1905
GEORGE B. LUKS
(AMERICAN, 1866–1933)
Oil on canvas, 36 x 26 in., 1931.9
Copyright © Addison Gallery of American Art, Phillips Academy, Andover, Massachusetts. All Rights Reserved.
Gift of anonymous donor